THE

SILLY
POEMS

THE HIPPO BOOK OF
SILLY
POEMS

COMPILED BY
JOHN FOSTER

Scholastic Children's Books,
Commonwealth House, 1–19 New Oxford Street
London WC1A 1NU, UK
a division of Scholastic Ltd
London ~ New York ~ Toronto ~ Sydney ~ Auckland

First published by Scholastic Ltd, 1998

ISBN: 0 590 19251 5

Printed by Cox & Wyman Ltd, Reading, Berkshire

5 7 9 10 8 6

Contents

So much for secret powers

Early last Tuesday I found I could fly,
so I jumped off our roof and looped loops in the sky.
Not a soul was astonished, or even impressed –
they just called out loudly, "Come down and get
    dressed."

Departing for school on the following morning
I turned into *triplets* without any warning.
But no one was awestruck or taken aback –
Mum simply observed, "That's *three* lunches to pack."

While doing my homework, succumbing to rage,
I drew a live creature that hopped off the page.
The only reaction from Dad was a mutter
of, "Darn! There's a dinosaur licking the butter."

At night, after dinner, my teeth all turned gold,
so I yelled at my parents, "I've gold teeth! Behold!"
They barely glanced up from the TV and said,
"Just make sure you brush them each night, before
    bed."

But on Thursday, at breakfast, at last they took note.
Dad stopped pouring coffee and Mum cleared her
    throat.
"How strange," they both murmured, "how curious,
    how weird —
Vicki, don't go to school till you've shaved off that
    beard."

Robin Klein

COME DOWN AND GET DRESSED

Aunty Aggie

Cleaning round the house one day,
Aunty Aggie went astray;
Sucked up by the vacuum cleaner,
Since which time, no one has seen her.
Where she is, there's just no knowing,
But when the thing was overflowing,
It seems to me without a doubt,
They simply threw the old bag out.

Mike Jubb

Auntie Dotty

My Auntie Dotty thought it nice
To twirl about upon the ice.
I warned her people of proportions
Such as hers, should take precautions.
But poor auntie was so fond
Of skating on the village pond,
That she did not heed my warning,
And went skating every morning.

Now we mourn for Auntie Dot:
The ice was thin, but she was not.

Colin West

11

Aunt Ermintrude

Aunt Ermintrude
was determined to
swim across the Channel.
Each week she'd
practise in the bath
encostumèd in flannel.

The tap end
was Cap Gris Nez
the slippy slopes
were Dover. She'd
doggypaddle up and down
vaselined all over.

After 18 months, Aunt Erm was in peak condition.
So, one cold grey morning in March
she boarded the Channel Steamer at Dover
went straight to her cabin
climbed into the bath
and urged on by a few well-wishers
Aunt Ermintrude, completely nude
swam all the way to France.
Vive la tante!

Roger McGough

Uncle

Uncle, whose inventive brains
Kept evolving aeroplanes,
Fell from an enormous height
On my garden lawn, last night.
　Flying is a fatal sport,
　Uncle wrecked the tennis court.

Harry Graham

Mary Mace

An artistic girl is Mary Mace
She paints in water-colours on her face.
Above her eye, the left I think,
Is a ballerina dressed in pink;
At the side of her nose and barely seen
A tiny portrait of the Queen;
On the other side and just as small
Blessing his flock is Pope John Paul;
Framed in gold on either cheek
Are statues of an ancient Greek;
Above the right eye Little Bo Peep
And on her chin the missing sheep.
In italic script her sister Rose
Prints the ten commandments on her toes.

Their master works last several hours
Then dissolve and fade when the girls take showers.

Jack Ousbey

Colonel Fazackerley

Colonel Fazackerley Butterworth-Toast
Bought an old castle complete with a ghost,
But someone or other forgot to declare
To Colonel Fazack that the spectre was there.

On the very first evening, while waiting to dine,
The Colonel was taking a fine sherry wine,
When the ghost, with a furious flash and a flare,
Shot out of the chimney and shivered, "Beware!"

Colonel Fazackerley put down his glass
And said, "My dear fellow, that's really first class!
I just can't conceive how you do it at all.
I imagine you're going to a Fancy Dress Ball?"

At this, the dread ghost gave a withering cry.
Said the Colonel (his monocle firm in his eye),
"Now just how you do it I wish I could think.
Do sit down and tell me, and please have a drink."

The ghost in his phosphorous cloak gave a roar
And floated about between ceiling and floor.
He walked through a wall and returned through a
    pane
And backed up the chimney and came down again.

Said the Colonel, "With laughter I'm feeling quite
    weak!"
(As trickles of merriment ran down his cheek.)
"My house-warming party I hope you won't spurn.
You must say you'll come and you'll give us a turn!"

At this, the poor spectre — quite out of his wits —
Proceeded to shake himself almost to bits.
He rattled his chains and he clattered his bones
And he filled the whole castle with mumbles and
    moans.

But Colonel Fazackerley, just as before,
Was simply delighted and called out, "Encore!"
At which the ghost vanished, his efforts in vain,
And never was seen at the castle again.

"Oh dear, what a pity!" said Colonel Fazack.
"I don't know his name, so I can't call him back."
And then with a smile that was hard to define,
Colonel Fazackerley went in to dine.

Charles Causley

Off Balance

I've got my nose to the grindstone.
I've got my back to the wall.
I've put my best foot forward.
I'm just about to fall.

John Kitching

The Sneeze and the Sniffle

The Sniffle sort of snuffled,
The Sob began to weep;
The Sigh looked grave,
The Snort was brave,
The Snore just went to sleep.

The Belch was loud and vulgar,
The Burp defined the issue;
The Gulp stood still,
The Gasp took ill,
The Sneeze cried out, "A TISSUE!"

Peter Wesley-Smith

The Diatonic Dittymunch

The Diatonic Dittymunch
plucked music from the air,
it swallowed scores of symphonies,
and still had space to spare,
sonatas and cantatas
slithered sweetly down its throat,
it made ballads into salads,
and consumed them note by note.

It ate marches and mazurkas,
it ate rhapsodies and reels,
minuets and tarantellas
were the staples of its meals,
but the Diatonic Dittymunch
outdid itself one day,
it ate a three-act opera,
and loudly passed away.

Jack Prelutsky

On the Ning Nang Nong

On the Ning Nang Nong
Where the Cows go Bong!
And the Monkeys all say Boo!
There's a Nong Nang Ning
Where the trees go Ping!
And the tea pots Jibber Jabber Joo.
On the Nong Ning Nang
All the mice go Clang!
And you just can't catch 'em when they do!
So it's Ning Nang Nong!
Cows go Bong!
Nong Nang Ning!
Trees go Ping!
Nong Ning Nang!
The mice go Clang!
What a noisy place to belong,
Is the Ning Nang Ning Nang Nong!

Spike Milligan

Careless

Diddle diddle dumpling, my son John
went to bed with his trousers on,
but what made people laugh and scoff
was his going to school with his trousers off.

Michael Dugan

Monday's Child is Red and Spotty

Monday's child is red and spotty,
Tuesday's child won't use the potty.
Wednesday's child won't go to bed,
Thursday's child will not be fed.
Friday's child breaks all the toys,
Saturday's child makes an awful noise.
And the child that's born on the seventh day
Is a pain in the neck like the rest, OK!

Colin McNaughton

Fee-Fi-Fo-Hum!

Fee-fi-fo-fum!
I smell the pong of an Englishman.
Be he alive or be he dead,
I wish he were somewhere else instead!

Colin McNaughton

Georgy Porgy Was Not Gorgy

Georgy Porgy
Pudding and pie
Kissed the girls
And made them cry
Here's why —

Georgy was a rubbish kisser
Gob like a frog
And lips like liver
His snogs were wetter
Than a major river
When he went up to girls
And said
"Fancy a snog?"
They'd start to quiver
9 out of 10 girls
Preferred to choose death
Than suffer Georgy's
Foul fishy breath.

Lindsay MacRae

There was an Old Maiden from Fife

There was an old maiden from Fife,
Who had never been kissed in her life;
Along came a cat,
And she said, "I'll kiss that!"
But the cat answered, "Not on your life!"

Anon

Lonely Hearts

Tired tabby, fluffy tail
Seeks a soft, unselfish male;
Must like munchies, fish and milk,
Cotton, beanbags, string and silk.

Tough old tomcat, dirty brown,
Fed up fooling
Round the town
Seeks someone with shiny fur
Maybe we can make a purr?

Mike Kivi

You Remind me of the Sea

"You remind me of the sea," he said,
"Deep, untamed and wild."
She sat there, looking modest,
Lovely, meek, and mild.

"What a strange coincidence,"
She answered smooth and slick.
"You remind me of the sea as well —
You always make me sick…"

Clive Webster

Cousin Nell

Cousin Nell
married a frogman
in the hope
that one day
he would turn into
a handsome prince.

Instead he turned into
a sewage pipe
near Gravesend
and was never seen again.

Roger McGough

Grounds for Recollection
(An old footballer remembers)

"Do you remember *Anfield*?" he asked.
Old Trafford nodded his head.
"She lived down near the *Maine Road*
By *St Andrew's* church," he said.

"*Molineux* her too," he said,
"They went to *St James's* school.
They once pretended to find a *Goldstone*.
They were always playing the fool.

"They tore down *The Shed* and built *The New Den*
In *The Dell* by *The Riverside*.
They used sticks they took from *The Hawthorns*
And *Turf* from the *Moor* inside.

"Once for a lark, in *Goodison Park*,
They made all of us boys go trembly
By claiming they'd found on the *City's Ground*
A Cup Final ticket for *Wembley*!"

John Foster

A Perfect Match

We met in Nottingham Forest,
    My sweet Airdrie and I.
She smiled and said, "Alloa!" to me —
    Oh, never say goodbye!

I asked her, "Is your Motherwell?"
    And she replied, "I fear
She's got the Academicals
    From drinking too much beer."

We sat down on a Meadowbank
    And of my love I spoke.
"Queen of the South," I said to her,
    "My fires of love you Stoke!"

We went to Sheffield, Wednesday.
    Our Hearts were one. Said she:
"Let's wed in Accrington, Stanley,
    Then we'll United be."

The ring was Stirling silver,
    Our friends, Forfar and wide,

A motley Crewe, all gathered there
    And fought to kiss the bride.

The best man had an awful lisp.
    "Come Raith your glatheth up,"
He said, and each man raised
    His Coca Cola Cup.

The honeymoon was spent abroad:
    We flew out east by Ayr,
And found the far-off Orient
    Partick-ularly fair.

We're home, in our own Villa now,
    (The Walsall painted grey)
And on our Chesterfield we sit
    And watch Match of the Day.

Pam Gidney

Basil Bragg

You may have heard of Basil Bragg
Who earns his living as a corner flag.
When Saturday home games come around
You'll find him down at the City Ground.
In the dressing room, as he makes the switch
From a human being to part of the pitch,
He really is a startling sight
In a body stocking painted white.
His tiny flag in Forest red
He screws down firmly in his head,
Then takes his place at a quarter to three —
A vital appurtenance is Basil B.
His brother Bert, so keen on horses,
Is a winning post at the major courses.

To those who fancy sporting action —
Unusual posts bring satisfaction.

Jack Ousbey

Helen the Hippo

Helen the Hippo was thrilled as could be
For tonight was her very first date
And so were her family, for single was she
And 92 stone over weight
Cried Helen, "He's handsome, he's asked me to dine
At 9 o'clock round at his place,"
And cleaning her teeth on a half-submerged tree
She put lots of hot mud on her face

Said her Mother, "Dear Helen, just where did you
    meet?
And did he remark on your size?"
Said her daughter, "While swimming and all he could
    see
Was my nose and my ears and my eyes
I fell in love with his splendid moustache
All plastered down with red mud
He fell in love with the parts he could see
And told me his first name was Dud."

Said her Father, "I think you should go for a run
You really should lose a few stone
Just fifteen or twenty could make all the difference
To marriage or living alone."
Poor Helen went running with tears in her eyes
The blazing hot sun on her back
But after ten miles she was still the same size
And her mud pack had started to crack

Like a large melting jelly she ran with a wobble
Another ten miles and she started to hobble
Wondering why she'd taken the trouble
For her chins were still treble, no sign of a double
Poor Helen just wept in the shade of a tree

For she knew that she'd never be lean
Then she heard the loud thunder of feet running by
It was Dudley all covered in steam
His splendid moustache drooped down to his knees
As did his stomach and chin
Then he slid to a halt and gasped with a wheeze
"It's no good I'll never be thin
Who'd want a lover who's quite so outsize?"
Said Helen, "Did somebody call?
And now we're together, the size of your thighs
Makes mine by comparison small."
Now they are married and happy as mud
With a big grown-up daughter called Kate
Who's got no idea with parents that size
That she's 92 stone over weight.

Jeremy Lloyd

God made penguins

God made penguins
    Minus knees
And filled them full
    Of antifreeze.

God made the rabbit,
    I'll teach you why –
To teach us all
    How to multiply!

God put wings
    On electric plugs –
There, in a twinkling,
    Lightning bugs!

God made the elephant
    A toothy mammal:
Short on molars,
    But long on enamel.

God took a potato
    The size of a bus —
And created a hippo-
    Potato-mus!

God made the rooster,
    God made the hen
But Ma made the chicken
    Pot pie. Amen!

J. Patrick Lewis

Look Back in Wonder

Though the Elephant's behind
Is delightfully designed
And the rump of any Rhino's mighty fine,
Though the buttocks of a Bear
Are indubitably fair
And the Pig is fundamentally divine,
Though the bum of any Bison
Is a singularly nice un,
And the backside of a Boa never stops –
Yet not one's got such a bottom as
The hugeous Hippopotamus.
For bottoms, Hippopotami are tops.

Dick King-Smith

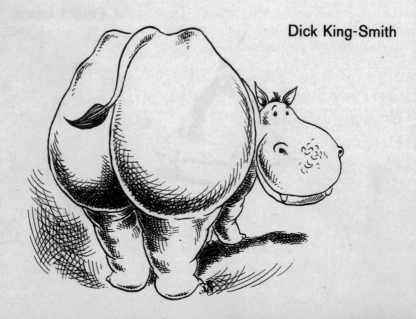

Hello Mr Python

Hello Mr Python
Curling round a tree,
Bet you'd like to make yourself
A dinner out of me.

Can't you change your habits
Crushing people's bones?
I wouldn't like a dinner
That emitted fearful groans.

Spike Milligan

39

Beware!
Beryl The Budgie

She's a seed eating, bell beating
Ball bashing, mirror smashing
Bully bird. Or haven't you heard of
Beryl The Budgie.

She wears a gold chain and a diamond ring
And carries a pistol, tucked under her wing.
She likes tight jeans and motorbike leathers
Unzipped to the navel to show off her feathers.

If you meet her in the street don't dare to speak
Unless she grants permission with a nod of her beak.
And never suggest that she's broken any laws
Or she'll break your neck with a twist of her claws.

She's done a few jobs, driving getaway cars
She got caught once; did time behind bars
But now she's out and earning a packet
Running a pet shop protection racket.

She's a seed eating, bell beating
Ball bashing, mirror smashing
Bully bird. Or haven't you heard of
Beryl The Budgie.

John Coldwell

The Panther

The panther is like a leopard,
Except it hasn't been peppered.
Should you behold a panther crouch,
Prepare to say Ouch.
Better yet, if called by a panther,
Don't anther.

Ogden Nash

The Octopus

If you should see an octopus
And stop him for a chat,
I warn you that an octopus
Will never raise his hat.
He'll boast of his accomplishments
In kingdoms underseas,
And then he'll bore you with complaints
Of water on the knees.

Peter Wesley-Smith

Plenty More Fish in the Sea

Do monkfish have habits
you'd better not mention
Do clownfish do tricks
just to get some attention

Do tuna like music
Do parrotfish squawk
Do sole put on shoes
to go out for a walk

43

Can angelfish fly
Are skate cold and icy
Do turbots have engines
is that why they're pricey

Do all fish have fingers
Do kingfish wear crowns
Is a haddock a hammock
who's let himself down

Do perch sit like budgies
Do carp mope about
Is a snapper bad-tempered
Do blowfish all pout

Do grouper get lonely
in groups less than three
Don't they know
that there's plenty more fish in the sea?

Lindsay MacRae

The Jumblies

They went to sea in a Sieve, they did,
   In a Sieve they went to sea;
In spite of all their friends could say,
On a winter's morn, on a stormy day,
   In a Sieve they went to sea!
And when the Sieve turned round and round,
And everyone cried, "You'll all be drowned!"
They called aloud, "Our Sieve ain't big,
But we don't care a button, we don't care a fig!
   In a Sieve we'll go to sea."

   Far and few, far and few,
     Are the lands where the Jumblies live;
   Their heads are green, and their hands are blue,
     And they went to sea in a Sieve.

They sailed away in a Sieve, they did,
   In a Sieve they sailed so fast;
With only a beautiful pea-green veil

Tied with a riband by way of a sail
  To a small tobacco-pipe mast;
And everyone said, who saw them go,
"O won't they be soon upset, you know,
For the sky is dark, and the voyage is long,
And happen what may, it's extremely wrong,
  In a Sieve to sail so fast."

  Far and few, far and few,
    Are the lands where the Jumblies live;
  Their heads are green, and their hands are blue,
    And they went to sea in a Sieve.

The water it soon came in, it did,
  The water it soon came in;
So to keep them dry, they wrapped their feet
In a pinky paper, all folded neat,
  And they fastened it down with a pin.
And they passed the night in a crockery jar,
And each of them said, "How wise we are!
Though the sky be dark and the voyage be long
Yet we never can think we were rash or wrong,
  While round in our Sieve we spin!"

Far and few, far and few,
   Are the lands where the Jumblies live;
Their heads are green, and their hands are blue,
   And they went to sea in a Sieve.

And all night long they sailed away;
   And when the sun went down,
They whistled and warbled a moony song,
To the echoing sound of a coppery gong,
   In the shade of the mountains brown.
"O Timballo! How happy we are,
When we live in a Sieve and a crockery jar,
And all night long in the moonlight pale,
We sail away with a pea-green sail
   In the shade of the mountains brown!"

Far and few, far and few,
   Are the lands where the Jumblies live;
Their heads are green, and their hands are blue,
   And they went to sea in a Sieve.

They sailed to the Western Sea, they did,
   To a land all covered with trees,
And they bought an Owl and a useful Cart,
And a pound of Rice and a Cranberry Tart,

And a hive of silvery Bees.
And they bought a Pig, and some green Jack-daws,
And a lovely Monkey with lollipop paws,
And forty bottles of Ring-Bo-Ree,
    And no end of Stilton Cheese.

Far and few, far and few,
    Are the lands where the Jumblies live;
Their heads are green, and their hands are blue,
    And they went to sea in a Sieve.

And in twenty years they all came back,
   In twenty years or more.
And everyone said, "How tall they've grown!
For they've been to the Lakes, and the Torrible Zone,
   And the hills of the Chankly Bore";
And they drank their health and gave them a feast
Of dumplings made of beautiful yeast;
And everyone said, "If we only live,
We too, will go to sea in a Sieve —
   To the hills of the Chankly Bore!"

Far and few, far and few,
   Are the lands where the Jumblies live;
Their heads are green, and their hands are blue,
   And they went to sea in a Sieve.

Edward Lear

49

The Disco Sheep

The disco sheep danced down the street.
He stomped his hooves to a disco bleat.

"I'm Sam the Ram. So form a queue.
I'll dance with ewe and ewe and ewe."

"I'm the best at The Hip Hop Skip.
You're number one at The Sheep Dip Trip."

"All you sheep wherever you are,
Shout Sam the Ram — Superbaah."

John Coldwell

The Tibetan Elephant

An elephant born in Tibet
One day in his cage wouldn't get.
   So its keeper stood near
   Stuck a hose in its ear,
And invented the first Jumbo Jet.

Anon

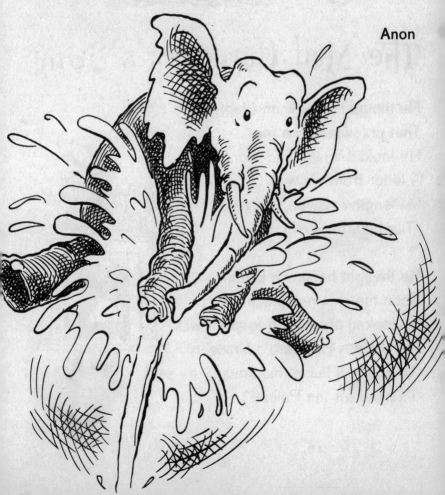

The Mad Gardener's Song

He thought he saw an Elephant,
That practised on a fife:
He looked again, and found it was
A letter from his wife.
"At length I realise," he said,
"The bitterness of Life!"

He thought he saw a Buffalo
Upon the chimney-piece:
He looked again, and found it was
His Sister's Husband's Niece.
"Unless you leave this house," he said,
"I'll send for the Police!"

He thought he saw a Rattlesnake
That questioned him in Greek:
He looked again, and found it was
The Middle of Next Week.
"The one thing I regret," he said,
"Is that it cannot speak!"

He thought he saw a Banker's Clerk
Descending from the 'bus:
He looked again, and found it was
A Hippopotamus.
"If this should stay to dine," he said,
"There won't be much for us!"

He thought he saw a Kangaroo
That worked a coffee-mill:
He looked again, and found it was
A Vegetable-Pill.
"Were I to swallow this," he said,
"I should be very ill!"

He thought he saw a Coach-and-Four
That stood beside his bed:
He looked again, and found it was
A Bear without a Head.

"Poor thing," he said, "poor silly thing!
It's waiting to be fed!"

He thought he saw an Albatross
That fluttered round the lamp:
He looked again, and found it was
A Penny-Postage-Stamp.
"You'd best be getting home," he said,
"The nights are very damp!"

He thought he saw a Garden-Door
That opened with a key:
He looked again, and found it was
A Double Rule of Three:
"And all its mystery," he said,
"Is clear as day to me!"

He thought he saw an Argument
That proved he was the Pope:
He looked again, and found it was
A Bar of Mottled Soap.
"A fact so dread," he faintly said,
"Extinguishes all hope!"

Lewis Carroll

A Horse in the House

There's a horse in the house, there's a horse in the
   house
It'll make Granny grumble and grizzle and grouse.
It made its way in through an open back door
And its hooves have made "U" shapes all over the
   floor.
Its response to requests to desist has been poor,
Surely someone can make it obey?

There's a horse in the lounge, there's a horse in the
   lounge!
Perhaps it's just hungry and here on the scrounge.
I've attempted to call it but don't know its name,
It's not Daisy or Dobbin or Clover or Flame
And I'm certain it thinks that the whole thing's a
   game,
Do you think we could bribe it with hay?

There's a horse in the hall, there's a horse in the hall
And the sight of it hasn't pleased Grandad at all.
He was sitting at peace in his old rocking chair
When he found himself facing an eighteen-hand mare

That's now clompety-clomping its way up the stair.
Does it think it's invited to stay?

There's a horse by my bed, there's a horse by my
    bed
And it's taken no notice whatever I've said.
I tried locking the rooms but it's kicked down each
    door
Then it looks down its nose as if I were a bore,
And drops food for the roses all over the floor
That it's my job to shovel away.

There's a horse on the roof, there's a horse on the
    roof
And the whole situation is way out of hoof
Aunt Aggie sat screaming on our mantelpiece
Now she's jumped down and rushed off to
    'phone the police
And they're charging the horse with a breach of the
    peace
(If it doesn't charge them on the way).

                                        Michael Day

The Flotz

I am the Flotz, I gobble dots,
indeed, I gobble lots and lots,
every dot I ever see
is bound to be a bite for me.
I often munch on myriads
of sweet, abundant periods,
I nibble hyphens, and with ease
chew succulent apostrophes.

From time to time, I turn my gaze
to little dotted "i's" and "j's,"
and if I chance upon a dash,
I soon dispatch it with panache.
I chomp on commas half the day,
quotation marks are rarer prey,
a semicolon's quite a treat,
while polka dots are joys to eat.
When I confront a dotted line,
my tongue flicks out, those dots are mine,

Morse code becomes a feast, and yes,
I've snacked upon an S.O.S.
For I'm the Flotz, who gobbles dots,
I gobble them in pails and pots,
and you'll not like my brief embrace
if you have freckles on your face.

Jack Prelutsky

Always Sprinkle Pepper

Always sprinkle pepper in your hair,
Always sprinkle pepper in your hair.
For then if you are kidnapped by a Wild Barbazzoop,
Who sells you to a Ragged Hag
Who wants you for her soup,
She'll pick you up and sniff you,
And then she'll sneeze "Achoo,"
And say, "My tot, you're much too hot,
I fear you'll never do."
And with a shout she'll throw you out,
And you'll run away from there,
And soon you will be safe at home a-sittin' in your
    chair,
If you always, always, always,
Always, always, always, always,
Always, always sprinkle pepper in your hair.

Shel Silverstein

For Neatness and Comfort

"For neatness and comfort,"
my grandfather said,
"Take off your boots
when you stand on your head."

"But," said Aunt Jane,
"does the boy understand
he should get a receipt
when he lends them a hand?"

"And have you implored him,"
inquired Aunt Sue,
"not to use toenails
where thumbtacks would do?"

"I have simply advised him,"
my grandfather said,
"to hold on to his hat
when he's losing his head."

N.M. Bodecker

Toe Names

Oh little toe, you tiny tot,
What shall we call you? "My name's Ot.
OT TOE."

The next toe gives advice to Ot.
"Always toe the line," says Mot.
MOT TOE.

Now we've reached the middle toe.
What a picture! This is Fo.
FO TOE.

Oh no it can't! Oh yes it can!
This toe can make you laugh. It's Pan.
PAN TOE.

Big toe now, a toe to note, a
Toe with two names. This is Po Tay.
PO TAY TOE.

("I know that's quite a mouthful, bud.
I tell my mates to call me Spud.")

Wendy Cope

Norman Norton's Nostrils

Oh, Norman Norton's nostrils
Are powerful and strong;
Hold on to your belongings
If he should come along.

And do not ever let him
Inhale with all his might,
Or else your pens and pencils
Will disappear from sight.

Right up his nose they'll vanish
Your future will be black.
Unless he gets the sneezes
You'll *never* get them back.

Colin West

Gastric 'Flu

Gastric 'Flu just isn't funny,
It's much, much, much, much, much
Too runny!

Susan Stranks

Never trust a lemon

Never trust a lemon –
it's a melon in disguise.
Never trust potatoes
with shifty eyes.
Never trust a radish –
it repeats all that it hears.
Never trust an onion.
It will all end in tears.

Roger Stevens

When the Coconut Got Run Over

When the coconut got run over,
There was chaos and confusion,
Till a passing milkman stopped his float
And gave it a milk transfusion.

Billy Brindle

Visiting the Museum

We tried hard to head him off
But alas he got there before us...

Never take a hungry dog
To see a brontosaurus.

Bill Condon

Flying Pizzas From Outer Space

Pizzas are falling from Outer Space,
They're flying, they're flying all over the place –
They float on the breeze
And zoom over trees,
Then land with a SPLAT
In my face.

Pizzas from Pluto,
Pizzas from Mars,
With cheese from the Moon
And dust from the stars.

I've had a whole heap of these pizzas —
Pizzas that fall from the sky,
Pizzas that hover and quiver,
Then land with a WHACK
In my eye.

Pizzas from Venus,
Pizzas from Mars,
With Jupiter toppings
And dust from the stars.

One day I may open a parlour
That serves up these pizzas from Space.
Till then I'll just eat them whenever
They land with a PLOP
In my face.

Pizzas from Saturn,
Pizzas from Mars,
With Mercury pastry
And dust from the stars.

Colin West

I'd Like to be a Teabag

I'd like to be a teabag,
And stay at home all day –
And talk to other teabags
In a teabag sort of way...

I'd love to be a teabag,
And lie in a little box –
And never have to wash my face
Or change my dirty socks...

I'd like to be a teabag,
An Earl Grey one perhaps,
And doze all day and lie around
With Earl Grey kind of chaps.

I wouldn't have to do a thing,
No homework, jobs or chores –
Comfy in my caddy
Of teabags and their snores.

I wouldn't have to do exams,
I needn't tidy rooms,

Or sweep the floor or feed the cat
Or wash up all the spoons.

I wouldn't have to do a thing,
A life of bliss — you see...
Except that once in all my life

I'd make a cup of tea!

Peter Dixon

71

Custard Day

On Custard Day
Most tea-cakes play,
And muffins are allowed, for once, to talk.
Mince pies dance –
They say in France
That even snails pick up their shells and walk.

On Custard Day,
So I've heard say,
All Food That's Not Been Eaten Yet Has Fun!
Hot dogs race,
And chips make lace,
And even dumplings stretch out in the sun.

Poached eggs sing,
Nuts play with string,
And buns roll round and round as if they're drunk.
Shallots go shopping,
Scones go bopping,
And cream éclairs go round collecting junk.

Meringues get tight,
Hamburgers fight,
Buttermilk and tarts and trifles flirt.
Cheeses tend
To find a friend
With whom they like to roll round in the dirt.

Waffles chatter,
Noodles natter,
Flapjacks, pancakes, pies and soup play chess.
Jam goes arty,
Cakes learn Karate,
And salads teach blancmanges how to dress.

On Custard Day,
Ice-cream goes gay.
Old doughnuts tell tall tales of things they've done.
Milk shakes rejoice,

Steaks find a voice.
All Food That's Not Been Eaten Yet Has Fun!

But on the day
After Custard Day,
You're better keeping safe at home in bed,
For that's when food
We've munched and chewed,
Comes back to celebrate its day instead!

Terry Jones

The Flying Spring Onion

The flying spring onion
    flew through the air
        over to where
the tomatoes grew in rows
    and he said to those
        seed-filled creatures
My rooted days are done,
    so while you sit here
        sucking sun
I'll be away and gone,

to Greenland
   where they eat no green
      and I won't be seen
in a salad bowl with you,
   stung by lemon,
      greased by oil,
and nothing at all to do
   except wait to be eaten.
With that he twirled
   his green propellers
and rose above the rows
   of red balls
who stared as he grew small
   and disappeared.

Matthew Sweeney

Solidarity

An army of militant greens
In bio-degradable genes
Shout, "Give peas a chance
And lettuce all dance
In unity wid butter beans."

Benjamin Zephaniah

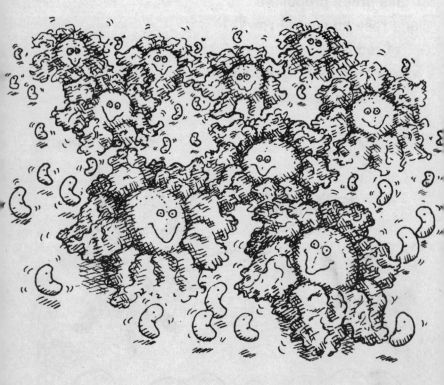

Teacher's Pet

Teacher's pet isn't Billy
or Darren or Sharon or Lee
Teacher's pet isn't Sally
or Vicky or Nicky or me
Teacher's hunting for her pet
She's crawling around on all fours
Teacher's pet is a big black spider
and she keeps it in her drawers.

Roger Stevens

A Late Night Drink

"A nightcap, sir?" the butler asked.
"A little drop of red?"
Dracula smiled and bared his teeth,
"If you don't mind," he said.
"I always like a little nip,
Before I go to bed!"

John Foster

Cockroach sandwich

Cockroach sandwich
  For my lunch
  Hate the taste
But love the crunch!

Colin McNaughton

I had a strange dream

"I had a strange dream,"
Vic said to his mum.
"I dreamed I was eating
This huge wine gum.

"It seemed to last all night.
It just went on and on.
I woke with this rubbery taste in my mouth
And the hot water bottle had gone!"

Billy Brindle

79

Two Sad

It's such a shock, I almost screech,
   When I find a worm inside my peach!
But then, what really makes me blue
   Is to find a worm who's bit in two!

William Cole

The old man of Blackheath

There was an old man of Blackheath
Who sat on a set of false teeth.
Said he, with a start,
"O, Lord, bless my heart!
I have bitten myself underneath!"

Anon

There was an old man of Darjeeling

There was an old man of Darjeeling
Who travelled from London to Ealing.
It said on the door,
"Please don't spit on the floor,"
So he carefully spat on the ceiling.

Anon

There was a young lady of Tottenham

There was a young lady of Tottenham,
Who'd no manners, or else she'd forgotten 'em.
At tea at the vicar's
She tore off her knickers
Because, she explained, she felt 'ot in 'em.

Anon

I sat next to the duchess at tea

I sat next to the duchess at tea
It was just as I feared it would be.
Her rumblings abdominal
Were simply phenomenal
And everyone thought it was me!

Anon

Nursery Epitaphs

Here lies the body
Of Contrary Mary,
Poisoned by milk
From the local dairy.

Here lies the body
Of Little Boy Blue —
Swallowed his horn
And it slid right through.

Here lies the body
Of Cinderella
Stabbed to death
By her sister's umbrella.

Here lies the body
Of Little Bo Peep,
Trampled to death
By a very large sheep.

Here lies the body
Of Little Jack Horner.

Ate too much Christmas pie
And dropped dead in his corner.

Here lies the body
Of Little Miss Muffet,
Bitten by a spider
Hiding in her tuffet.

Here lies the body
Of Winnie the Pooh.
He poohed too much
And died in a zoo.

Here lies the body
Of Mr Toad,
Squashed by a lorry
On a very busy road.

John Kitching

Acknowledgements

The editor and publishers gratefully acknowledge the following for permission to reproduce copyright poems in this book:

"For neatness and comfort" by N.M. Bodecker from *Hurry, Hurry, Mary Dear*, published by J.M. Dent, reprinted by permission of The Orion Publishing Group Ltd; "When the coconut got run over" and "I had a strange dream last night" by Billy Brindle, reprinted by permission of the author; "Colonel Fazackerley" by Charles Causley from *Collected Poems*, published by Macmillan, reprinted by permission of David Higham Associates Ltd; "The Disco Sheep" © John Coldwell and "Beware Beryl the Budgie", first published in *The Slack-Jawed Camel* by John Coldwell published Stride 1992, reprinted by permission of the author; "Visiting the Museum" by Bill Condon from *Don't Throw Rocks at Chicken Pox*, published by Angus and Robertson, reprinted by permission of the author; "Toe Names" by Wendy Cope reprinted by permission of the author; "A Horse in the House" by Michael Day reprinted by permission of the author; "I'd like to be a tea bag" by Peter Dixon reprinted by permission of the author; "Careless" by Michael Dugan reprinted by permission of the author; "Grounds for Recollection © 1997 John Foster, "A late night drink" © 1997 John Foster, included by permission of the author; "A Perfect Match" by Pam Gidney, first published in *You'll Never Walk Alone*, ed. David Orme, published Macmillan Children's Books 1995, reprinted by permission of the author; "Custard Day" by Terry Jones reprinted by permission of Pavilion Books from *The Curse of the Vampire's Socks* by Terry Jones; "Auntie Aggie" by Mike Jubb reprinted by permission of the author; "Look Back in Wonder" © 1990 by Fox Busters Ltd. Extracted from *Jungle Jingles* by Dick King-Smith published by Picture

Index of authors' names

Index of Titles